# *Supporting* **Writing Skills**

## *FOR AGES* **10–11**

**Andrew Brodie**

# Introduction

*Supporting Writing Skills* is aimed at all those who work with children who have been identified as needing 'additional' or 'different' literacy support. It can be used by anyone working with children who fall into this category, whether you are a teacher, classroom assistant or parent.

Typically the ten to eleven year-old children for whom the book is intended will be working at the levels expected of Year 5 children or may simply need extra help in tackling the level of work appropriate for Year 6. Their difficulties may be short term, and overcome with extra practice and support on a one-to-one or small group basis, or they may be long term, where such support enables them to make progress but at a level behind their peer group. The *Record and Review* sheet on page 5 is ideal for keeping track of the targets you set and the progress made by each child.

The activities in this book provide exactly what the children need – plenty of writing activities linked to their work in other aspects of literacy. All the activities provide great opportunities for speaking and listening and these sometimes include simple drama activities based on role-play. Most pages include reading practice in addition to the main writing task. Each activity page includes brief Notes for teachers so that the pages can be picked up and used quickly and effectively.

The 2006 Framework for teaching Literacy lists twelve strands for literacy development. Strands 1 to 4 concern Speaking and Listening; Strands 5 to 12 concern Reading and Writing. The writing activities in this book have been created to match many of the key elements of the Framework's Reading and Writing strands for Year 3, Year 4, Year 5 and Year 6:

5. Our activities reflect the move from word recognition to language comprehension but we recognise that some lower ability pupils will still need some support with decoding and encoding

6. Spell high frequency and medium frequency words; spell unfamiliar words using known conventions including grapheme-phoneme correspondences and morphological rules; develop a range of personal strategies for learning new and irregular words

7. Infer consequences in logical explanations; using syntax, context and word structure to build their store of vocabulary as they read for meaning; compare different types of narrative and information texts and identify how they are structured

8. Empathise with characters; interrogate texts to deepen and clarify understanding and response

9. Make decisions about form and purpose; use beginning, middle and end to write narratives in which events are sequenced logically and conflicts resolved; write non-narrative texts using structures of different text types; select and use a range of technical and descriptive vocabulary; use settings and characterisation to engage readers' interest; reflect independently and critically on their own writing and edit and improve it; experiment with different narrative forms and styles to write their own stories; adapt non-narrative forms and styles to write fiction or factual texts; vary the pace and develop the viewpoint through the use of direct and reported speech, portrayal of action and selection of detail

10. Signal sequence, place and time to give coherence; group related material into paragraphs; use adverbs and conjunctions to establish cohesion within paragraphs

11. Compose sentences using adjectives, verbs and nouns for precision, clarity and impact; punctuate sentences accurately, including using speech marks and apostrophes

12. Write with consistency in the size and proportion of letters and spacing within and between words, using the correct formation of handwriting joins.

Children generally achieve the greatest success in an atmosphere of support and encouragement. Praise from a caring adult can be the best reward for the children's efforts. The worksheets and activities in this book will provide many opportunities for children to enjoy these successes. The development of a positive attitude and the resulting increase in self-esteem will help them with all of their school work and other areas of school life too.

This book consists of three main sections:

## Section 1 (pages 6–28)

Worksheets 1 to 23 provide opportunities for creating simple and complex sentences. Examples of sentences with clear punctuation are provided for the pupils and the accompanying activities involve the construction of accurate sentences that start with capital letters and end with full stops. A letter writing activity is used to demonstrate how writing is a purposeful activity and to provide practice of clear layouts, including paragraphs. Many activities include the use of more advanced punctuation: speech marks, question marks and exclamation marks.

Several pages include dictation exercises. These help children both to identify the sounds in particular words to assist with their spelling and to 'hear' the punctuation. By listening carefully to the dictated sentences, the children can spot where to use full stops, commas, exclamation marks and question marks.

## Section 2 (pages 29–48)

Worksheet 24 to 36 address two specific forms of writing: non-fiction and fiction. The writing of instructions is the focus for non-fiction and creating a scary story is the focus for fiction.

Five writing templates (44–48) are also included that are suitable for a variety of opportunities for written work such as formal and informal letters, a tri-fold leaflet and illustrated stories.

## Section 3 (pages 49–64)

An important resource contained within this book is the dictionary that can be created from the final fourteen sheets. This contains all the high frequency words recommended for Key Stage 1 and the medium frequency words for Key Stage 2, together with all the additional words used in the books in this series. The dictionary can be used by the child when working on the worksheets.

Most pages of the dictionary have spaces for the child to write her/his own spellings – this is an excellent way of encouraging the child to use her/his phonic knowledge to spell new words. When a child needs a word, help her/him to find the correct page of the dictionary then ask her/him to attempt the word by segmenting it into its phonemes. Give the child lots of praise where s/he is successful even in part of a word then write the word correctly on the line next to her/his attempt, stressing the phonemes and pointing out the graphemes that represent these.

## Strands of objectives for Literacy in the Primary Framework

On the Contents page we have listed which strand each worksheet addresses.

1. Speaking

2. Listening and responding

3. Group discussion and interaction

4. Drama

5. Word recognition: decoding (reading) and encoding (spelling)
   (Note: this strand ceases to be used after year2/year3)

6. Word structure and spelling

7. Understanding and interpreting texts

8. Engaging with and responding to texts

9. Creating and shaping texts

10. Text structure and organisation

11. Sentence structure and punctuation

12. Presentation

# Contents

# Record and Review

Name: _____    Date of birth: _____

Teacher: _____    Class: _____

Support assistant: _____

---

Code of Practice stage: _____    Date targets set: _____

Target

**1** _____

**2** _____

**3** _____

**4** _____

---

Review

Target

**1** _____

_____

_____    Target achieved? ☐ Date: _____

**2** _____

_____

_____    Target achieved? ☐ Date: _____

**3** _____

_____

_____    Target achieved? ☐ Date: _____

**4** _____

_____

_____    Target achieved? ☐ Date: _____

**Name:** _____  **Date:** _____

Write a description of yourself.

**First paragraph:** Write obvious things such as your name, whether you are a boy or a girl and what school you go to.

**Second paragraph:** Write about your family, where you live and whether you have any pets at home.

**Third paragraph:** Write about what you like doing and who your friends are.

**Fourth paragraph:** Write about what you don't like doing!

**Final paragraph:** Write about the future. Which secondary school you hope to go to, what you are looking forward to and what you are a bit nervous about.

_____

_____

_____

_____

_____

_____

_____

_____

_____

_____

_____

_____

_____

**Notes for teachers**

This worksheet provides lots of opportunities for getting to know a new pupil. Discuss the paragraph instructions thoroughly before helping her/him to write the description. Some children will need lots of prompts for each paragraph. When s/he is ready to start, help her/him to compose complete sentences and then write them down, remembering capital letters and full stops as appropriate. Some of the words needed can be found in the dictionary created from the Resource sheets on pages 51–64. The child, with your help, can enter other new words in the dictionary.

**Andrew Brodie: Supporting Writing Skills © A & C Black Publishers Ltd. 2007**

**Name:**                                              **Date:**

Seth has just started at a new school
and has met his new teacher.
Read the conversation that they had.

"Hello Seth. My name is Mrs Turner. I am pleased to meet you,"
said Mrs Turner.

"Hello Mrs Turner," said Seth politely.

"I hope that you will like this school. Did you like your last one?"
asked Mrs Turner.

"It was all right but there was too much writing to do," replied Seth.

"Don't you like writing?" asked Mrs Turner.

"Not much," said Seth.

"Don't worry, we will give you lots of help," said Mrs Turner.

---

**Notes for teachers**

This worksheet provides revision of work covered in previous books in this series and is designed as an introductory
worksheet, to be used before dictating the last part of the conversation using Worksheet 3. You may like to role-play this
conversation with the child first. To do this successfully it's a good idea to highlight each speaker's comments in a different
colour, colouring only the words that are spoken i.e. the words contained within the speech marks.
Now look at the sentences carefully with the child. Encourage her/him to notice that:
• the spoken words are contained between the speech marks
• every sentence starts with a capital letter
• the sentences do not end at the end of the spoken section
• the closing speech marks are never alone – they always have a comma or a question mark before them
• different words are used before the speaker's name e.g. 'said', 'asked', 'replied'
• a new line is started where a different person speaks.
When you think the child is ready give her/him a copy of Worksheet 3.

Listen to your teacher. Write the conversation between Mrs Turner and Seth. The conversation has been started for you.

"Hello Seth. My name is Mrs Turner. I am pleased to meet you," said Mrs Turner.

"Hello Mrs Turner," said Seth politely.

"I hope that you will like this school. Did you like your last one?" asked Mrs Turner.

_____

_____

_____

_____

_____

_____

_____

_____

_____

_____

_____

_____

**Notes for teachers**
This worksheet should be used after Worksheet 2. You may decide to show the child Worksheet 2 again during the course of the dictation. Before dictating the conversation to the child, remind her/him of the 'rules' for writing down the conversation (Worksheet 2). You may need to dictate the conversation several times. Encourage the child to write using the school's handwriting style. As an extension activity, the child could continue the conversation in her/his own words.

          *Andrew Brodie: Supporting Writing Skills © A & C Black Publishers Ltd. 2007*

Look at this very short conversation:

"Good morning," said Mr Aziz.

"Hello, how are you?" asked Mr Jones.

Here are some rules about writing conversations:

1. The spoken words are contained between speech marks.

2. Every sentence starts with a capital letter.

3. The sentences do not end at the end of the spoken section.

4. The closing speech marks are never alone – they always have a comma, an exclamation mark, a full stop or a question mark before them.

5. Different words are used before the speaker's name e.g. 'said', 'asked', 'replied'.

6. A new line is started where a different person speaks.

Continue the conversation between Mr Aziz and Mr Jones. You don't need to write very much but you do need to follow the rules very carefully.

_____

_____

_____

_____

_____

_____

_____

**Notes for teachers**

The child will already have heard the 'rules' for writing speech when working on Worksheets 2 and 3 but, for the first time, those rules are written out for her/him to read. Help her/him to read them and to match each rule to examples in the written conversation. S/he may need some help in thinking of extra comments that Mr Aziz and Mr Jones could make to each other. Encourage the child to write neatly in accordance with the school's policy for joined handwriting.

Do you remember the rules for writing conversations?
On this sheet you are going to write a conversation between two people.
Choose your first character and give her or him a name.

a teacher    a nurse    a shopkeeper    a coffee-seller    a boy    a girl

Now choose your second character and give her or him a name.

a teacher    a doctor    a customer    a head teacher    a boy    a girl

Try to think of a conversation that your two characters might have.
When you are ready, write down the conversation. Don't forget the rules
for conversations!

_____

_____

_____

_____

_____

_____

_____

_____

_____

**Notes for teachers**

Once the child has selected her/his two characters you may need to provide suggestions for what the people could be discussing. Ideally you could role-play the conversation with the child. Encourage her/him to follow both the school's handwriting policy and the conversation 'rules' when writing the conversation. Watch the child as s/he writes the sentences, prompting her/him to remember speech marks, capital letters, exclamation marks, etc. If s/he finds any of the spellings difficult encourage her/him to look up the words in the dictionary created from the Resource sheets on pages 51–64. Give lots of praise for any success.

Look at all these snippets of conversations.

"Where are you?" called Sam.

"How are you today?" asked Jasdeep.

"It's a lovely day," said Mum.

"I've lost my shoe!" cried Jess.

"Get down from there!" shouted the teacher.

"Very well, thank you," replied Tariq.

"Help!" yelled the boy who was stuck up a tree.

"Bring me your book," demanded the teacher.

"The baby's asleep," whispered Gran.

"No sugar, thank you," answered the builder.

Now look at this piece of conversation.

"Hello," said the teacher.

This is a verb to show speaking.

Write the 'speech verb' from each snippet of conversation.

_____ _____ _____ _____ _____

_____ _____ _____ _____ _____

These are good words to use to make your writing more interesting.

---

**Notes for teachers**

This worksheet provides reading practice as well as plenty of opportunities for speaking and listening. Help the child to read the spoken sentences. Discuss the verbs used for speaking shown in these sentences i.e. called, asked, said, shouted, demanded, replied, whispered, answered, cried and yelled. There are several extension activities that the child could complete:

• try to compose a response to go with each of the sentences provided e.g. to go with the first sentence, "I'm over here," said Kate.
• think of some more verbs used for speaking
• think of words that are related to the speech verbs e.g. ask, asking, asked.
• search through her/his reading book to find more speech verbs.

Look again at the speech verds that you found on Worksheet 6.

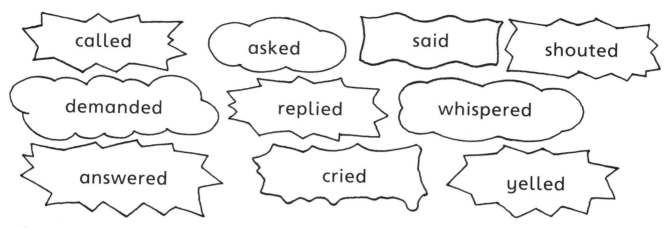

Make up a conversation between you and a friend then write it down using as many of the speech verbs as you can.

There were ten speech verbs on Worksheet 6. Can you use at least five of them in your written conversation?

_____
_____
_____
_____
_____
_____
_____
_____
_____
_____
_____
_____
_____
_____
_____

**Notes for teachers**

Read through the 'speech verbs' with the child then help her/him to compose an imaginary conversation with a friend. You may decide to encourage her/him not to use the noisier verbs such as 'shouted' or 'yelled'! Remind her/him of the 'rules' for writing down conversations, perhaps by looking again at Worksheet 4 together. Watch the child as s/he writes the sentences, prompting her/him to remember speech marks, capital letters, exclamation marks, etc. If s/he finds any of the spellings difficult encourage her/him to look up the words in the dictionary created from the Resource sheets on pages 51–64. Give lots of praise for any success.

**Name:** _____  **Date:** _____

Look at this short sentence.

> ## Tom walked slowly into the room.

This word is a verb telling us what Tom was doing.

This word is an adverb. It is added to the verb 'walked' and tells us <u>how</u> Tom walked.

Write six more short sentences about Tom. In each sentence use a verb and an adverb to say what Tom did and how he did it.

_____

_____

_____

_____

_____

_____

_____

_____

**Notes for teachers**

Read through the worksheet with the child, making sure that s/he understands what to do. S/he may need help in thinking up ideas. The illustration provides one idea for a sentence such as _Tom climbed carefully up the ladder_. You could suggest that s/he starts each sentence with the name Tom then writes a verb, e.g. Tom ran, Tom walked, Tom rushed, Tom jumped, Tom spoke, Tom rolled, Tom hopped, Tom fell. Ask the child to think of an adverb to go with each verb, then to complete each sentence by, for example, considering where Tom was or whom he was with. When s/he is ready to write the sentences down encourage the child to 'hear' the phonemes in the words so that s/he is able to segment the words to spell them. If s/he finds any of the spellings difficult encourage her/him to look them up in the dictionary created from the Resource sheets on pages 51–64. Remind the child to write neatly using handwriting that follows the school's policy.

Look at this sentence.

This word is a verb telling us what Tom was doing first.

This word is an adverb. It is added to the verb 'walked' and tells us <u>how</u> Tom walked.

This word is a conjunction. It is used to join two parts of a sentence together.

> Tom walked slowly into the room and sat crossly on the chair.

This word is a verb telling us what Tom did next.

This word is an adverb. It is added to the verb 'sat' and tells us <u>how</u> Tom sat.

Write out the sentence again but change how things happened, by using different adverbs.

_____

_____

Now write your own two-part sentence.

_____

_____

**Notes for teachers**

Read together the sentence about Tom's entry into the room then discuss the notes that are provided to explain some of the words in the sentence. Remind the child that all sentences must have at least one verb but that this one has two. Discuss the conjunction 'and', pointing out that this single sentence could have been written as two separate sentences: *Tom walked slowly into the room. He sat crossly on the chair*. Help the child to change the sentence about Tom simply by substituting different adverbs e.g. Tom walked quickly into the room and sat quietly on the chair. Other possible adverbs include calmly, carefully, thoughtfully, sensibly. As a final activity read through the sentences that the child has created. Can s/he 'hear' the punctuation? You can help children to understand where full stops should appear by encouraging them to listen to the tone of voice of your voice at the end of a sentence.

Look again at Worksheets 8 and 9. On Worksheet 8 you made up lots of sentences about Tom and on Worksheet 9 you saw how a sentence can have two parts if you use the conjunction and. On this page you are going to make up your own short story about Tom.

Rules for this story!

Your story must have at least ten sentences.

Every sentence must have at least one verb with an adverb.

Your story must be about Tom.

Tom must go somewhere in the story – you must decide where he goes.

Something must happen – you must decide what.

Tom must speak to somebody – you must decide whom.

Your story must have an ending.

_____
_____
_____
_____
_____
_____
_____
_____
_____
_____
_____
_____

**Notes for teachers**

Read through the sheet with the child, making sure that s/he understands what to do. Look again at Worksheets 8 and 9 as these will help the child to think of ideas. Discuss where Tom could be going, whom he could be speaking to, what happens then and how the story could end. Remind the child of the rules for writing conversation, when s/he reaches that part of the story. When s/he is ready to write the story, encourage the child to 'hear' the phonemes in the words so that s/he is able to segment the words to spell them. If s/he finds any of the spellings difficult encourage her/him to look up the words in the dictionary created from the Resource sheets on pages 51–64. Give lots of praise for any success with this difficult task. As an extension activity, if the child has not used paragraphs other than those for the speech, you could look through the story with the child to identify where paragraphs change. S/he could then rewrite the story using her/his best handwriting on a separate piece of paper (Writing template 2 on page 45 will be very useful for this).

**Name:** _____          **Date:** _____

You are going to create a leaflet about your school that could be used to encourage parents to send their children there.

Your first task is to describe your class. Here are some things to think about:

Who is your teacher?

Do any other adults work with your class?

How many girls and how many boys are there in your class?

What ages are the pupils in your class?

What subjects do you study in the classroom?

Are there any subjects that you study elsewhere? For example, do you have PE in the hall?

Do you have class trips?

Now write your description. Remember to use interesting sentences.

_____

_____

_____

_____

_____

_____

_____

_____

_____

_____

**Notes for teachers**

This worksheet provides the first activity in the eventual creation of an advertising leaflet about your school. You may like to use Worksheets 11 to 15 over several lessons, culminating in the production of a tri-fold leaflet that can be created from the writing template. Read through the questions with the child, encouraging her/him to discuss her/his class. S/he may have her/his own ideas and these should be encouraged. When s/he is ready help her/him to write the description. Ensure that s/he uses full sentences with appropriate punctuation.

**Name:** _____ **Date:** _____

You are going to create a leaflet about your school that could be used to encourage parents to send their children there.

Your second task is to describe another class in your school. Here are some things to think about:

Who is the teacher?

Do any other adults work with the class?

How many girls and how many boys are there in the class?

What ages are the pupils in the class?

Does the class have any aspects that are different to your own class?

Now write your description. Remember to use interesting sentences.

_____
_____
_____
_____
_____
_____
_____
_____
_____
_____
_____
_____

**Notes for teachers**

This task will be easier if the child chooses a class that is very different from her/his own class e.g. a Key Stage 1 class. Read through the questions with the child, encouraging her/him to discuss the class. It would be a good idea for her/him to visit the chosen class for research purposes, noting features of the class such as play equipment. When s/he is ready help her/him to write the description. Ensure that s/he uses full sentences with appropriate punctuation and that s/he follows the school's handwriting policy.

**Name:** _____     **Date:** _____

You are going to create a leaflet about your school that could be used to encourage parents to send their children there.

Your next task is to describe your school. Here are some things to think about:

What is the name of your school?

Where is your school? What road is it in? Is it near anywhere special?

What is the age range of the school?

Who is your head teacher?

Which other adults are parents or children likely to meet?

How many girls and how many boys are there in the whole school?

How many classrooms are there?

What other buildings are there?

Now write your description. Remember to use interesting sentences.

_____

_____

_____

_____

_____

_____

_____

_____

_____

_____

_____

**Notes for teachers**

This worksheet provides the third activity in the creation of an advertising leaflet about your school. Read through the questions with the child, encouraging her/him to discuss the school buildings and the key personnel in the school. Remind her/him that everybody is important but that the leaflet cannot include all members of staff and should include the people who parents and children are likely to have most contact with. S/he may have her/his own ideas and these should be encouraged. When s/he is ready help her/him to write the description. Ensure that s/he uses full sentences with appropriate punctuation.

   

You are going to create a leaflet about the school that could be used to encourage parents to send their children there.

Your next task is to describe the school grounds. Here are some things to think about:

How many playgrounds do you have?

Are the playgrounds for everybody's use?

Do you have a school field? If so, what is the field used for? Does it have football posts? Is it marked for sports activities?

Do you have any gardens at school?

Does the school have any special features in the grounds, such as a pond?

Does the school have a fence, a hedge or a wall?

Now write your description. Remember to use interesting sentences.

_____

_____

_____

_____

_____

_____

_____

_____

_____

_____

**Notes for teachers**

This worksheet provides the fourth activity in the creation of an advertising leaflet about your school. Read through the questions with the child, encouraging her/him to discuss the school grounds and outdoor facilities. S/he may have her/his own ideas and these should be encouraged. When s/he is ready help her/him to write the description. Ensure that s/he uses full sentences with appropriate punctuation and that s/he follows the school's handwriting policy.

**Name:** _____     **Date:** _____

You are going to create a leaflet about your school that could be used to encourage parents to send their children there. You are now ready to plan the leaflet.

The type of leaflet that you are going to produce is called a tri-fold leaflet. The prefix tri means 'three'. You will see that the piece of paper that makes the leaflet is folded into three sections and these give you six areas to work on in total because you can work on both sides.

Plan what you are going to show on each of the six areas of your leaflet.

**Notes for teachers**

This worksheet provides the final activity in preparation for producing a tri-fold leaflet about the school. Before the lesson, photocopy two sides of a piece of paper using Writing template 5 on page 48 and show the child the blank tri-fold leaflet that this produces. Ensure that the child understands that the paper is folded twice to create three sections but that these three sections allow for six areas of work. Help her/him to decide which is the front of the leaflet, then how the other areas will appear. Now help her/him to use this worksheet to plan what information should be shown on each area e.g. the name of the school, the buildings, the grounds, descriptions of at least two classes, etc. When s/he is ready give her/him the tri-fold sheet on which to present the finished leaflet. If possible, encourage her/him to show the finished version to the head teacher so that s/he feels that her/his work is gaining a special audience.

**Name:**                                          **Date:**

Mrs Reece is thinking about sending her son to a new school. She has written a letter to the head teacher of Upper Creech Primary School, Miss Wilkinson. The letter below has been jumbled up. Sort out the letter into the correct order, then stick most of the pieces on to Worksheet 17. There is one extra piece. Give that piece to your teacher.

I am writing to ask if you have any spaces available in your school for my son, Alex, who is eleven years old. We are moving to Creech Street in Denborough on 1st November and would like Alex to start at your school on Monday 5th November if possible.

Yours sincerely,
Amanda Reece

| | |
|---|---|
| 3 Grange Gardens<br>Overley<br>Denborough<br>DB3 9EE | Miss Wilkinson<br>Head teacher<br>Upper Creech Primary School<br>Creech Street<br>Denborough<br>DB5 2ZU |

12th October 2007

I would be very pleased if you could send me some information about your school. Please let me know if you would have a space for Alex. I look forward to hearing from you.

Dear Miss Wilkinson,

Alex is currently at Overley Primary School where he is very happy. He does find writing rather difficult but is making a lot of improvement by trying very hard.

**Notes for teachers**

It is important to point out to the child that this is an imaginary letter and that the people and school referred to are not real, especially if there is a child in your school with the same surname as either of those used. This worksheet provides reading practice as well as plenty of opportunities for speaking and listening. Some of the words are extremely difficult to read and the child will need a lot of help. Discuss the fact that this is a formal letter and therefore includes the recipient's address as well as the sender's address. Note also the use of 'yours sincerely' rather than something less formal such as 'best wishes' because the writer does not know the person to whom s/he is writing. Help the child to sort the letter into the correct order, encouraging her/him to read each piece out loud to you. When s/he is ready, allow her/him to stick the pieces in the correct places on Worksheet 17 but keep hold of the third paragraph of the text so that you can dictate it for the child to copy.

**Name:**                                     **Date:**

Stick the pieces from Worksheet 16 in the correct places. One paragraph is missing. Listen to your teacher to help you to write that paragraph.

**Notes for teachers**

Help the child to stick the pieces of the formal letter from Worksheet 16 in the correct places. Dictate the third paragraph of the letter to the child, reading each sentence slowly and clearly. Help the child to 'hear' the phonemes in the words so that s/he is able to segment the words to spell them. If s/he finds any of the spellings difficult encourage her/him to look up the words in the dictionary created from the Resource sheets on pages 51–64.

Read again the letter from Mrs Reece to Miss Wilkinson on Worksheet 17. You are now going to play the part of Miss Wilkinson and write a reply to Mrs Reece.

Imagine that you are the head teacher of Upper Creech Primary School. Your name is Miss Wilkinson! You have received a letter from Mrs Reece. You need to decide what she wants and make up some sentences that will tell her what she needs to know. You could offer to send her a leaflet about your school.
Make some notes about what you are going to tell Mrs Reece.

_____

_____

_____

_____

_____

_____

_____

_____

_____

_____

_____

_____

_____

_____

**Notes for teachers**
This worksheet should be used after Worksheets 15 to 17. Before starting this task, photocopy Writing template 4 on page 47. This should be paper-clipped to a piece of plain paper and can be used by the pupil when s/he is ready to write the letter. Help the child to read the instructions on this page and to re-read the complete letter from Mrs Reece on Worksheet 17. Help the child to think up ideas of what to write in the letter; perhaps s/he could ask the head teacher what s/he would write in reply to such a letter? When s/he is ready give her/him the plain paper with the guidelines attached and ask her/him to write a neat letter with clear sentences and good spelling. Suggest that s/he makes use of the dictionary created from the Resource sheets on pages 51–64.

**Name:** _____  **Date:** _____

Imagine that a new boy, Alex Reece, is going to start at your school soon and that your teacher has asked you to write a letter to welcome him. What could you write?

You could tell Alex all about your school. You could tell Alex all about yourself and your friends.

You could make him feel welcome by saying that he can play with you and your friends at break-time.

You could tell him all about your lessons, such as which ones you like and which ones you are not so keen on.

You could tell him about school trips that you have had and school plays that your school has done.

Write down some ideas.
Remember, your letter will be informal, not like the letter that Miss Wilkinson sent to Mrs Reece.

_____

_____

_____

_____

_____

_____

_____

_____

_____

_____

**Notes for teachers**
This worksheet follows Worksheets 15 to 18. Before starting this task, photocopy Writing template 3 on page 46. This should be paper-clipped to a piece of plain paper and can be used by the pupil when s/he is ready to write the letter. Read through the questions and suggestions with the child, encouraging her/him to think of her/his own ideas. When s/he is ready give her/him the plain paper with the guidelines and ask her/him to write a neat letter with clear sentences and good spelling. Suggest that s/he makes use of the dictionary created from the Resource sheets on pages 51–64.

Name: _____    Date: _____

# A Motorway Accident

## Notes for teachers

This worksheet provides a great opportunity for speaking and listening. Discuss the picture with the child: 'What has happened?' 'How did it happen?' 'What is each person doing?' 'What is each person saying?' 'What is going to happen next?' Help the child to think of answers to these questions before giving her/him a copy of Worksheet 21. Worksheets 22 and 23 also feature follow-on work in relation to this picture and, as well as these, there are many opportunities for extension activities: radio reports about the accident, newspaper reports, conversations between adults stuck in the traffic jam, conversations between children and their parents, etc.

**Name:** _____    **Date:** _____

Look at the picture on Worksheet 20.

**1.** What has happened?

_____

_____

_____

**2.** How did it happen, do you think?

_____

_____

_____

**3.** What is each person doing?

_____

_____

_____

_____

_____

**4.** What is going to happen next?

_____

_____

_____

**Notes for teachers**
Remind the child of the answers that s/he thought of when you were discussing the picture together. Help her/him to phrase appropriate sentences in response to the written questions. Encourage her/him to write neatly, using the school's handwriting style, to punctuate accurately and to attempt to spell all the words needed, perhaps by referring to the dictionary created from the Resource sheets on pages 51–64. As an extension activity help the child to compose a story about the picture. Read through with her/him the responses that s/he wrote above, then put the worksheet to one side and ask her/him to create a story using the picture as a stimulus. Encourage her/him to write a title at the top of the story and to write in paragraphs.

Andrew Brodie: Supporting Writing Skills © A & C Black Publishers Ltd. 2007

After the accident the lorry driver decided to telephone his boss.
Here is the start of their conversation written like a play script.

Lorry driver: Hello Boss. I'm afraid there's been a bit of an accident.

Boss: What have you done now?

Lorry driver: It wasn't my fault.

Boss: Tell me what happened.

Lorry driver: Well, I was just driving along when my phone rang so I leaned over to pick it up off the dashboard and the next thing I know I'm swerving all over the place. I don't know what happened really.

Boss: It's obvious what happened. You shouldn't have answered your phone. Is everything ok now?

Lorry driver: Not too bad.

Boss: Was anybody hurt?

Lorry driver: No.

Boss: What about the load of paint?

_____

_____

_____

_____

_____

_____

_____

_____

**Notes for teachers**

The child has already experienced conversations written in the form of direct speech. Explain to her/him that the conversation on this sheet is shown as a play script so does not need speech marks. Read the script with her/him, first with you taking the role of the lorry driver and the child taking the role of the boss then swap roles and read it through again. Point out that the lorry driver hasn't really given a full explanation for the chaos that he has caused then discuss how the conversation might have continued. Help the child to write a few more lines of the conversation in the form of a play script. As an extension activity you could ask the child to rewrite part of the conversation as direct speech.

Read this report about what the police did when they first arrived at the accident.

Police Constable Helen Groves was one of the first police officers to arrive at the scene of the accident. She called her control centre to tell them about the accident. She told the officer at the control centre, PC Dave Harris, that a lorry had swerved sharply so that its load had tipped out over the road. PC Harris asked her what the load was and she told him that it was tins of paint. He said to her that it must be quite messy and she agreed that it was and that some of the tins had opened so that there was paint on the road. He asked her if all three lanes of the motorway were affected and she explained that they were but that the hard shoulder was clear.

Now read the passage below where the same report has been started again. Can you see the different way that it has been presented?

Police Constable Helen Groves was one of the first police officers to arrive at the scene of the accident. She called her control centre to tell them about the accident.

"Hello, this is PC Helen Groves calling from an accident near junction 26 of the M5," said Helen.

"Hello, you are speaking to PC Dave Harris. What has happened?" asked Dave.

"A lorry has shed its load onto the carriageway," replied Helen.

"What was in the load?" asked Dave.

_____

_____

_____

_____

_____

_____

**Notes for teachers**
The child has already experienced conversations written in the form of direct speech and as a script. Explain that the short report on this worksheet includes a *description* of a conversation but does not use the actual words spoken and for this reason it is called 'reported speech' or 'indirect speech'. Help the child to read the passage and to identify which sentences relate to the conversation that PC Groves had with PC Harris. Now discuss the second passage and help the child to identify the use of direct speech. Point out that the first two sentences are unchanged as they are not part of the conversation. Ask the child to continue the conversation using direct speech.

# Notes for teachers on Worksheets 24 to 30

The next seven worksheets focus on writing instruction text and are intended for use by pupils working in pairs with a teacher or assistant. On Worksheets 24 to 27 two sets of instructions are provided for the pupils to follow and they result in the completion of a simple jigsaw and the creation of a paper aeroplane. The purpose of these instructions is to enable the pupils to analyse the features of written instructions before writing their own i.e. there is usually a verb at or near the beginning of each instruction, instructions are often numbered to ensure they are completed in the correct order and diagrams are used where appropriate to aid the understanding of each step. It is also useful to discuss the type of sequencing words that may be at the beginning of some instructions before the verb e.g. first, next, finally etc.

**Worksheet 24** features a set of instructions that lead to the making of a twenty-piece jigsaw. Help pupils to notice that instructions are not written in the form of flowing sentences, and that many instructions appear to be in a note form. Ask pupils where they have seen instructions in everyday life e.g. recipes, game playing instructions, etc. If possible have some sets of instructions from a variety of sources for children to look at.

**Worksheets 25 and 26** each have 10 puzzle pieces to be cut out. These pages will need to be copied on to card for best results. The completed puzzle will measure approximately 35cm by 24cm. Pupils should glue the finished puzzle on to a piece of A3 paper and may decide to colour it. When completed, the puzzle will contain a set of instructions for making a paper aeroplane.

**On Worksheet 27** there is an aeroplane template for pupils to use when following the instructions on the jigsaw. You may decide to ask pupils to experiment with different ways of folding the aeroplane's tail, of weighting the aeroplane and of launching it. Now ask each child to write a set of instructions on how to make the aeroplane fly well.

**Worksheet 28** contains a new set of instructions for the pupils to arrange in the correct order and to match to the diagrams provided on Worksheet 29. They can then discuss whether diagrams are helpful in that particular set of instructions. They are also asked to pick out a poorly written instruction and to replace it with a better one of their own. This is of course instruction number 5 that states *Your dog will enjoy being rubbed down with a towel.* Ask pupils to say why this is not a good instruction. (It does not begin with a verb, it tells you what a dog will enjoy not what you must do.) Ask children to talk about how this could be improved before they write it in the space provided. They should volunteer something like *Rub dog with towel.* There may of course be some variation.

**Worksheet 30** asks the pupils to write a set of instructions for making a jam sandwich. Diagrams are given to act as a set of sequencing ideas for this activity. It is ideal, if possible, for pupils to try following their instructions exactly to see if they work and the end result of eating a sandwich may provide great motivation for writing!

Name: _____          Date: _____

The instructions below will help you to make a jigsaw.
Before you follow the instructions underline the verb in each one.
What do you notice about where each verb is written?

How to complete a jigsaw

1. Carefully cut out the pieces from Worksheets 25 and 26.

2. Place the pieces, face up, on a tray.

3. Find the four corner pieces and put them in position. (You may need to look at the picture to help you).

4. Next take out the edge pieces. (They are the pieces with one straight edge).

5. Now join the edge pieces to make the outside of the puzzle.

6. Fit the other puzzle pieces into the correct places to complete the jigsaw.

7. Glue your completed jigsaw on to a sheet of paper.

8. Colour the pictures on the jigsaw.

9. Finally follow the instructions on the puzzle to make yourself a paper aeroplane.

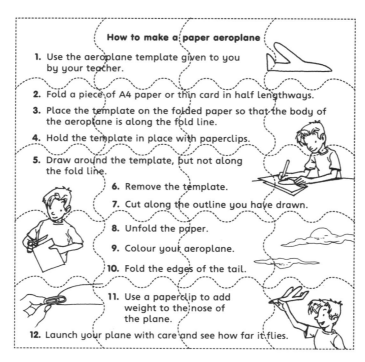

**How to make a paper aeroplane**

1. Use the aeroplane template given to you by your teacher.

2. Fold a piece of A4 paper or thin card in half lengthways.

3. Place the template on the folded paper so that the body of the aeroplane is along the fold line.

4. Hold the template in place with paperclips.

5. Draw around the template, but not along the fold line.

6. Remove the template.

7. Cut along the outline you have drawn.

8. Unfold the paper.

9. Colour your aeroplane.

10. Fold the edges of the tail.

11. Use a paperclip to add weight to the nose of the plane.

12. Launch your plane with care and see how far it flies.

          Andrew Brodie: Supporting Writing Skills © A & C Black Publishers Ltd. 2007

Cut out the jigsaw pieces carefully.

gthways.

the body of

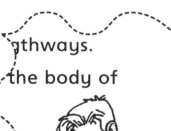

nd the template, [
e.

6. Remove the te

7. Cut along t

2. Fold a piece

3. Place the t
   the aeropl

4. Hold the ten

5. Draw arou
   the fold lin

of A4 paper or th

mplate on the fol

ane is along the f

plate in place wit

paper aeroplane

ven to you

n card in half leng

ded paper so that

old line.

h paperclips.

How to make a

plane template gi
cher.

1. Use the aero
   by your tea

**Name:** _____    **Date:** _____

Cut out the jigsaw pieces carefully.

...per.

...aeroplane.

...s of the tail.

8. Unfold the po...

9. Colour you...

10. Fold the edge...

...ve drawn.

...but not along

...emplate.

...he outline you ha...

...lip to add

...nose of

...and see how far it...

...flies.

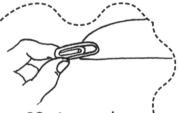

12. Launch yo...

11. Use a paperc...
    weight to the...
    the plane.

...ur plane with care...

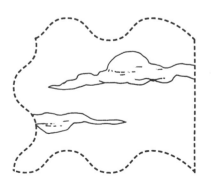

Andrew Brodie: Supporting Writing Skills © A & C Black Publishers Ltd. 2007

**Name:** _____ **Date:** _____

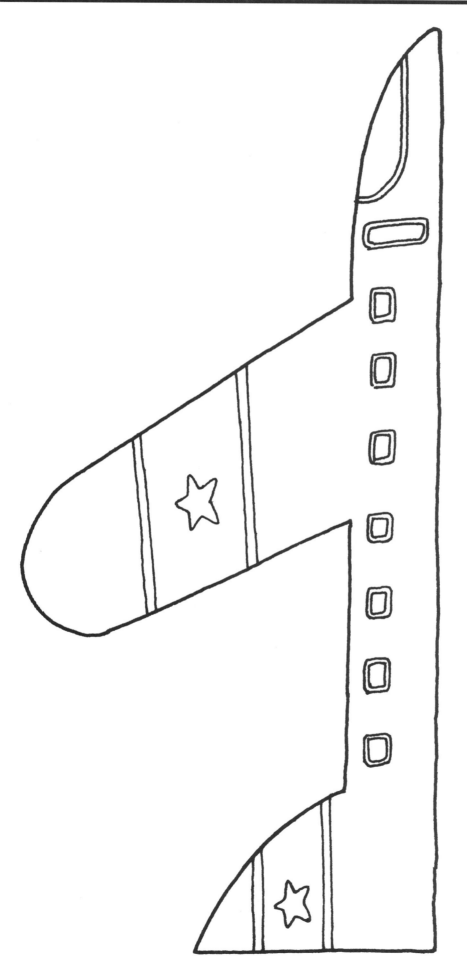

33

**Name:** _____     **Date:** _____

Read the instructions below, which are not in the correct order.
One of them is not written correctly. Decide which one then write it in a
better way in the box at the bottom of the page.
Cut out each instruction and the diagrams on Worksheet 29.
Now try to match the instructions to the diagrams and to put them all
into the correct order.

| | | |
|---|---|---|
| Rinse off the shampoo. | Brush your dog and keep him somewhere warm until he is completely dry. | Carefully rub dog shampoo into the dog's fur. |
| Remove the dog from the bath. | Put the dog in an empty bath. | Your dog will enjoy being rubbed down with a towel. |
| Gently shower the dog with warm water. | Stand well back while the dog shakes his fur. | _____ _____ _____ _____ |

How to bath
a dog

The frame below is for you to write a set of instructions on how to make a jam sandwich. The diagrams have been done for you.

Remember to:

Keep your instructions clear and simple.

Number them.

Use a verb as the first or second word.

*Andrew Brodie: Supporting Writing Skills © A & C Black Publishers Ltd. 2007*

# Notes for teachers on Worksheets 31 to 36 and the Writing templates

The next six pages deal with fiction writing and culminate in the production of a 'scary story'. Pupils are supported in choosing a main character and a setting for their story; they are given a selection of suitable words for their writing in this genre; they are given the opportunity to explore ways to vary their setting for the greatest effect and they are given a planning structure to produce a story, which can be completed using Writing template 1 on page 44. It is anticipated that this work will take several sessions to complete and give lower attaining pupils the satisfaction of having produced a high standard of work through reflecting, editing and improving.

**Worksheet 31** enables pupils to build a character profile. Features of the character are created by rolling a dice and selecting an attribute from the corresponding box. The child should then draw a picture of her/his main character in the frame provided on Worksheet 32. There is a large speech bubble in which the pupil can write a few lines as if the character is introducing her/himself. This part of the task allows the child to further personalise the character and to write about her/him in the first person.

**Worksheet 33** enables the child to find some ideas for the story's setting in terms of place and time and to decide on one or more extra characters for the story.

**Worksheet 34** is a story-planning sheet. It encourages the child to consider other aspects of their story including what event or events happen in the body of the story and how the story is resolved. Help the child to think of ideas for the scary event and for the ending of the story. Before completing this sheet it is important for the child to recap what s/he has done so far and to talk about what s/he would like the plot of the story to be. Ensure that the child understands that this planning sheet is used only to write words, phrases or simple sentences, not for writing whole sections of story.

**Worksheet 35** shows a variety of ways to begin a story. This page can be used as a 'stand alone' activity looking at ways to open a particular genre of story, though on another occasion you may decide to let the child continue and complete a story based on one of the 'story starts'. The first story start gives most of the basic details needed to set the scene but lacks the language that helps the reader to engage with it as a scary tale. The others give a variety of details and use some language suitable for the genre. The final one does not tell the reader that the boy is entering a house, so an important piece of information has been missed. It is important for the child to realise that when opening a story it is more important to engage the reader than it is to include every detail of the scene setting, though the most important features must be present. These possible beginnings could be the focus of a group activity in which pupils could make a list of what information about the story has been included. This list should include: Taran aged 12 (main character), old house (possibly haunted), dark evening, one week (time passed since start of story), something surprising in house. Encourage children to use appropriate language to enhance their own attempt at a start for a story.

**Worksheet 36** has a selection of suitable vocabulary to support pupils' writing. You may wish to add to this list. This sheet can be used throughout this work.

## Writing templates

Writing template 1 can be photocopied to make a one-page A4 story sheet to be used at any time you would like the child to produce a narrative or non-narrative piece of writing. The child can draw a picture at the top of the sheet then use the writing lines to write her/his own story.

Writing template 2 can be photocopied so the child can paperclip it behind a sheet of plain paper enabling her/him to write neatly without having to use lined paper.

Writing template 3 can be used in the same way to create guidelines for writing an informal letter and Writing template 4 provides similar guidelines but for a formal letter.

Writing template 5 should be photocopied onto both sides of A4 paper and can then be used to create a tri-fold leaflet.

**Name:** _____  **Date:** _____

You are going to plan and write a scary story.

The first part of your planning for this story is to decide on a main character. Rolling a dice will help you to choose a character and to decide some aspects of your character's appearance. Look at the three sets of boxes below. Each box has a number. When you roll the dice the number will tell you which box to choose. If you prefer, you can make a choice from each set instead of rolling the dice. Each time you choose a feature of your character you can colour the picture that goes with it.

## Character

| 1 man | 2 woman | 3 young girl | 4 young boy | 5 teenage boy | 6 teenage girl |

## Hair

| 1 short dark straight hair | 2 long dark straight hair | 3 curly dark hair | 4 curly blond hair | 5 short straight blond hair | 6 long straight blond hair |

## Face

| 1 blue eyes, cheerful face | 2 brown eyes, cheerful face | 3 blue eyes, sad face | 4 brown eyes, sad face | 5 blue eyes, thoughtful face | 6 brown eyes, thoughtful face |

What is the name of your main character? _____

Andrew Brodie: Supporting Writing Skills © A & C Black Publishers Ltd. 2007

Draw a picture of your main character. Write some phrases that your character could say about him or herself. These could be about the character's name, age, appearance, occupation, etc.

(Do you know what etc means? It is short for et cetera, which is Latin and means 'and the rest' or 'and so on'.)

# A picture of my character

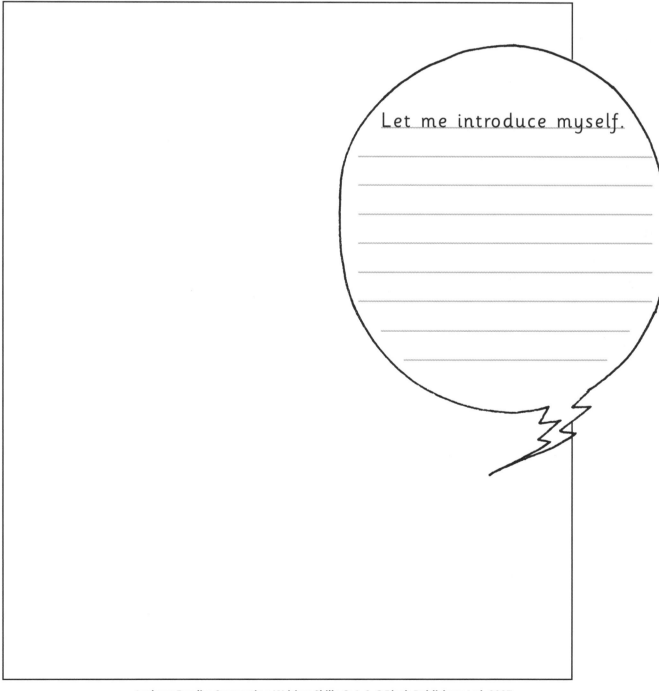

Let me introduce myself.

**Name:** 

**Date:** 

Rolling a dice will help you to choose the setting for your scary story and to decide who the extra characters could be.

Look at the three sets of boxes below. The first two sets are about the setting of your story: where and when it takes place. The third set helps you to introduce some extra characters.

Each box has a number. When you roll the dice the number will tell you which box to choose. If you prefer, you can make a choice from each set instead of rolling the dice. Write the choices you made on Worksheet 34.

## Place

| an old house | the woods | a mansion | a windmill | the seafront | an attic |

## Time

| early one evening | late one evening | early one morning | in the middle of the night | after school | one afternoon |

## Other characters

| a good friend | two friends | three friends | a sister | a brother | a stranger |

You have a main character, important extra characters, the place and the time when your story begins. Now you can start to plan more about what will happen in the rest of your story.

You can also think of a good title for your story.

This page will help you to do the planning. Remember you are only planning – you are not writing the finished story yet!

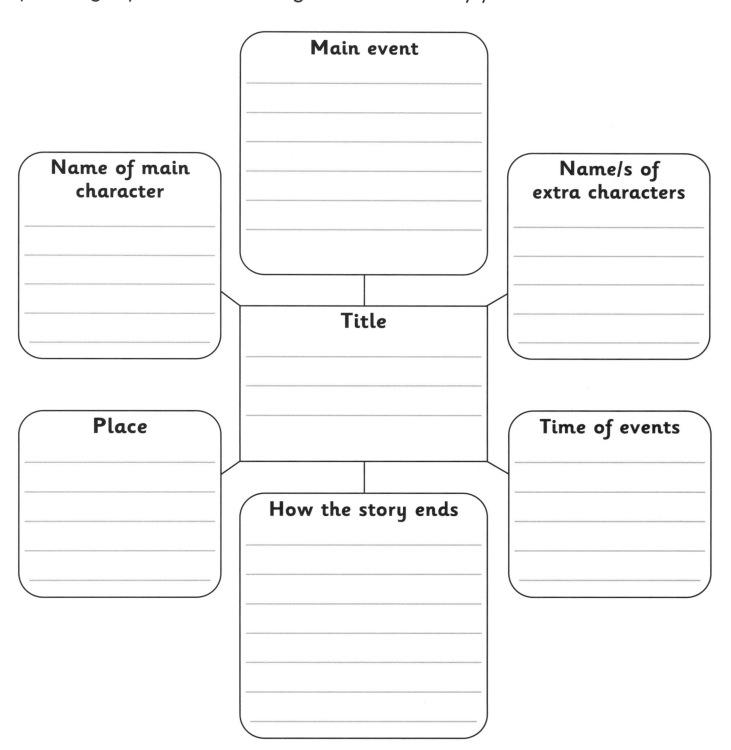

Andrew Brodie: *Supporting Writing Skills* © A & C Black Publishers Ltd. 2007

**Name:**                                                           **Date:**

Before you start to write your scary story, read the three paragraphs below.

They are all possible beginnings for a scary story.

Which one do you think is best and why?

Talk about it with a partner, your teacher or in a group.

It was one evening about a week ago that the story started. It began with a twelve year-old boy called Taran who went into an empty house. The children who lived nearby thought the house was haunted but Taran went in to show how brave he was.

The house was eerily quiet on that dark evening. Taran was beginning to regret boasting that he was brave enough to go into it alone. He crept warily through the open front door and stepped into the gloomy hallway. Taran gasped when he realised what was in front of him.

Taran's hand trembled as he slowly pushed open the door. He stepped into the cold silent darkness. Little did he know what he would find inside. Was it really just one week ago when this tale of horror began?

How would you start your story?

Have a go in the space below.

Any of these words might be found in a scary story. Are any of them suitable for your story?

| | | | |
|---|---|---|---|
| chilling | creak | creaked | creaking |
| creaky | | | |

| | | | |
|---|---|---|---|
| dark | | | |

| | | | |
|---|---|---|---|
| escape | escaped | escaping | eerie |
| eerily | eeriness | | |

| | | | |
|---|---|---|---|
| fear | fearful | fright | frighten |
| frightened | | | |

| | | | |
|---|---|---|---|
| gloom | gloomy | | |

| | | | |
|---|---|---|---|
| haunt | haunted | haunting | |

| | | | |
|---|---|---|---|
| night | | | |

| | | | |
|---|---|---|---|
| scare | scared | scary | scream |
| screamed | screaming | shadow | shadows |
| shadowy | shiver | shivered | shivering |
| shriek | shrieked | shrieking | spine tingling |
| spook | spooky | strange | |

| | | | |
|---|---|---|---|
| tremble | trembled | trembling | |

| | | | |
|---|---|---|---|
| yell | yelled | yelling | |

# Writing template 1

# Writing template 2

**Notes for teachers**
This sheet can be photocopied and given to the child to be fastened with paper-clips behind an A4 sheet of plain paper. This will enable the child to write neatly without having to use lined paper.

Andrew Brodie: Supporting Writing Skills © A & C Black Publishers Ltd. 2007

45

This is where you write your
own address.
Make sure that you spell
it correctly and that
you include the postcode.

This is where you write the date.

Dear ...

_____

_____

_____

_____

_____

_____

_____

_____

_____

_____

_____

_____

Here you can write Yours sincerely, or Best wishes, or Love from,.

This is where you write your name.

### Notes for teachers

This sheet can be photocopied and given to the child as an informal letter template. Talk about each part of the page before asking the child to fasten it with paper-clips behind an A4 sheet of plain paper. S/he should be able to see the lines through the sheet of plain paper and this will enable her/him to write neatly without having to use lined paper.

# Writing template 4

This is where you write your own address.
Make sure that you spell it correctly and that you include the postcode.

This is where you write the name and address of the person or the company you are writing to.

This is where you write the date

Dear ... person's name, or Sir or Madam,

_____

_____

_____

_____

_____

_____

_____

_____

_____

_____

_____

_____

Here you can write Yours sincerely, or Yours faithfully,.

This is where you write your name.

## Notes for teachers

This sheet can be photocopied and given to the child as a formal letter template. Talk about each part of the page before asking the child to fasten it with paper clips behind an A4 sheet of plain paper. S/he should be able to see the lines through the sheet of plain paper and this will enable her/him to write neatly without having to use lined paper. Explain that, as this is for a formal letter, s/he needs to show the name and address of the person or company to whom s/he is writing on the left-hand side. When s/he reaches the end of the letter s/he should write 'Yours sincerely' if s/he has used the person's name or 'Yours faithfully' if s/he has not used a person's name.

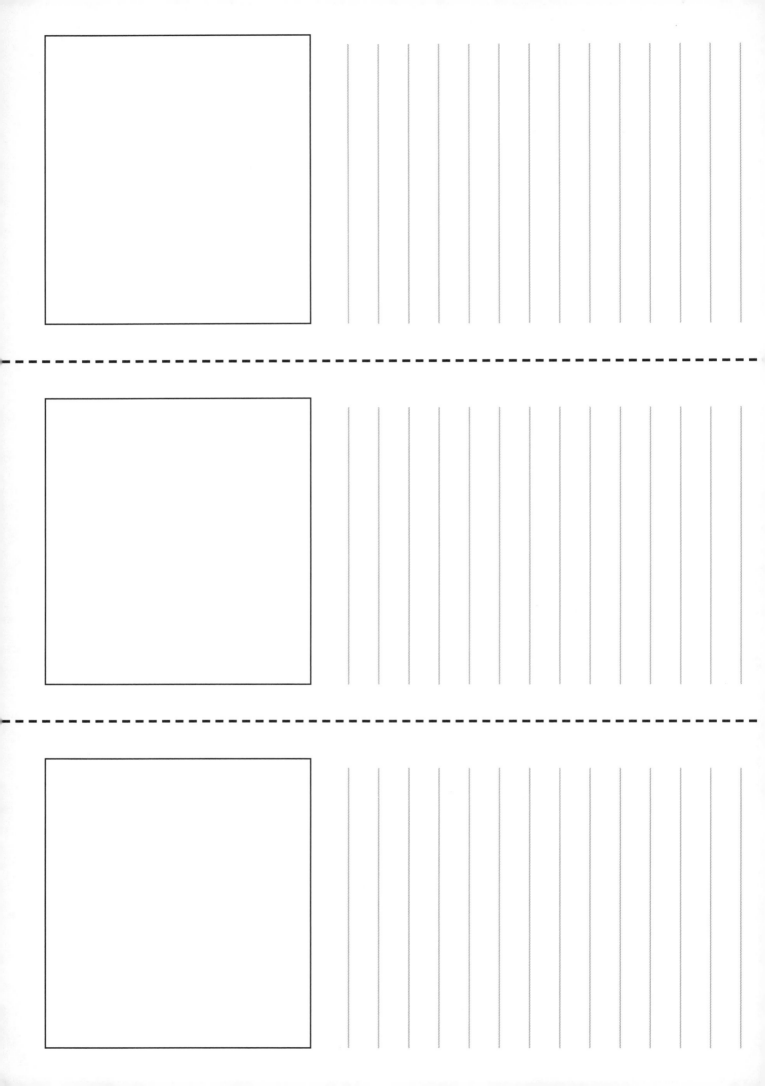

# Notes for teachers on the Dictionary resource sheets

The dictionary that can be created from the final fourteen pages of this book is a very valuable resource. You may like to practise the alphabet with the child before helping her/him to make the dictionary. An alphabet practice sheet is provided on page 50. Photocopy the fourteen Dictionary resource sheets to create master copies then photocopy the master copies, back to back, as follows:

Sheets 1/ 2    Sheets 3/4    Sheets 5/6    Sheets 7/8    Sheets 9/10    Sheets 11/12    Sheets 13/14

The dictionary contains all the high frequency and medium frequency words recommended for Key Stages 1 and 2, together with many of the additional words used in other books in this series.

Each page of the dictionary has spaces for pupils to write their own spellings. This is an excellent way of encouraging children to use their phonic knowledge to spell new words. When a child needs a word help her/him to find the correct page of the dictionary, then ask her/him to attempt the word by segmenting it into its phonemes. Give the child lots of praise where s/he is successful even with part of a word, then write the word correctly on the line next to her/his attempt, stressing the phonemes and pointing out the graphemes that represent these.

# Alphabet Practice sheet

How quickly can you join the pairs of letters?
Draw a line to connect the **a** to the **A**, then another line to join
the **b** to the **B** and so on for the rest of the alphabet.
Time yourself.

## Notes for teachers

Read the sentences with the child, pointing out the question mark at the end of the question sentence. Revise the alphabet with the child, saying the names of the letters and the sounds that they make. Help her/him to draw lines to join the lower case letters to the matching upper case letters. This must be completed in alphabetical order. Set the challenge of completing the task as quickly as possible. This task can be repeated several times if appropriate as it encourages the child to practise alphabetical order. It is essential that s/he can recognise the capital letter equivalent of each lower case letter. Take the opportunity to introduce the dictionary created from the Resource sheets on pages 51–64, if you have not already done so. A further time challenge could be to see how quickly the child can locate a particular page in this dictionary e.g. How quickly can s/he find the k page, the p page, the m page, etc?

Andrew Brodie: Supporting Writing Skills © A & C Black Publishers Ltd. 2007

# Dictionary resource sheet 1

# Dictionary

Name _____

---

| Days | Months | Numbers | |
|------|--------|---------|---|
| Monday | January | 1 | one |
| Tuesday | February | 2 | two |
| Wednesday | March | 3 | three |
| Thursday | April | 4 | four |
| Friday | May | 5 | five |
| Saturday | June | 6 | six |
| Sunday | July | 7 | seven |
| | August | 8 | eight |
| | September | 9 | nine |
| | October | 10 | ten |
| | November | 11 | eleven |
| | December | 12 | twelve |
| | | 13 | thirteen |
| | | 14 | fourteen |
| | | 15 | fifteen |
| | | 16 | sixteen |
| | | 17 | seventeen |
| | | 18 | eighteen |
| | | 19 | nineteen |
| | | 20 | twenty |

# Dictionary resource sheet 2

**Name**

**Address**

## The alphabet

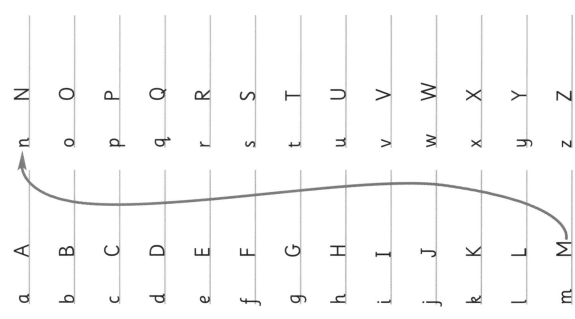

| a A | n N |
| b B | o O |
| c C | p P |
| d D | q Q |
| e E | r R |
| f F | s S |
| g G | t T |
| h H | u U |
| i I | v V |
| j J | w W |
| k K | x X |
| l L | y Y |
| m M | z Z |

# Dictionary resource sheet 3

## a A

a
able
about
above
abroad
accident
achieve
across
activities
activity
address
adjective
adult
adventure
adverb
affect
afraid
after
afternoon
again
aircraft
alarm

alien
all
allowed
all right
almost
alone
along
also
always
am
an
and
animals
another
answer
answered
any
anyway
anywhere
apartment
appearance
apple
are

area
arm
around
arrive
arrived
as
ask
asked
asking
aspect
assistant
at
attic
Australia
autumn
available
average
away

## x X

## y Y

year
yell
yelled
yelling
yellow
yes
you
young
your
yourself

## z Z

zero
zip

# Dictionary resource sheet 4

| b  B | | w  W | |
|------|------|------|------|
| baby | broken | Wales | what |
| back | brother | walk | when |
| ball | brought | walked | where |
| balloon | brown | walking | while |
| banana | build | wall | whisper |
| bark | builder | want | white |
| barked | building | warily | who |
| battery | bulb | was | whole |
| be | bungalow | watch | why |
| beard | business | water | will |
| beautiful | busy | way | window |
| because | but | we | winter |
| bed | by | wear | wire |
| been | | wearing | wish |
| before | | weed | wishes |
| began | | week | with |
| being | | weekend | without |
| below | | weight | woke |
| best | | welcome | woken |
| better | | went | woman |
| between | | were | women |
| bicycle | | west | wood |
| big | | | word |
| bike | | | work |
| birthday | | | world |
| bite | | | worry |
| biting | | | would |
| bits | | | wrap |
| black | | | write |
| blond | | | writing |
| blue | | | wrong |
| boast | | | wrote |
| boat | | | |
| bonfire | | | |
| bored | | | |
| both | | | |
| bottom | | | |
| boy | | | |
| branch | | | |
| brave | | | |
| break | | | |
| breakfast | | | |
| brick | | | |
| bright | | | |
| bring | | | |

Andrew Brodie: Supporting Writing Skills © A & C Black Publishers Ltd. 2007

# Dictionary resource sheet 5

## v | V

vegetables
vehicles
verb
very
village

## c | C

| call | city | constable |
|---|---|---|
| called | clean | container |
| came | clean-shaven | continue |
| camera | clear | control |
| can | climb | conversation |
| can't | climbing | corner |
| canines | close | correct |
| caravan | clothes | cost |
| carefully | cloudy | costume |
| cat | coat | could |
| catch | coffee | couldn't |
| caught | colour | countries |
| centre | coloured | country |
| cereals | come | crazily |
| chair | comes | crazy |
| change | coming | crew |
| character | company | cricket |
| chase | compensation | cried |
| cheek | complain | cries |
| cheerful | complaining | cross |
| chew | complaint | cruise |
| children | complete | cry |
| chin | computer | curly |
| choose | confirmation | currently |
| cinema | conjunction | customer |
| | consider | |

# Dictionary resource sheet 6

## d  D

dad

dangerous

dark

dashboard

day

daytime

decide

decided

demand

describe

description

diagram

dice

did

didn't

different

dig

direct

distance

do

doctor

does

dog

don't

door

down

downstairs

dressed

drop

dropped

drove

during

## u  U

ugly

unconscious

under

uniform

United Kingdom

until

up

upon

upstairs

us

used

# Dictionary resource sheet 7

## t T

| | | |
|---|---|---|
| tail | think | towel |
| take | thinking | town |
| tall | third | train |
| teach | this | transport |
| teacher | those | trap |
| teaches | thought | trapping |
| teenage | thoughtful | travel |
| teeth | thoughtfully | travelling |
| telephone | three | tree |
| television | through | tremble |
| template | ticket | tried |
| tenth | tile | tries |
| than | time | tri-fold |
| thank | tiny | trip |
| that | tired | tripped |
| the | to | trotting |
| their | today | trousers |
| them | together | trunk |
| then | told | trust |
| there | tongue | tumbled |
| these | too | turn |
| they | took | turned |
| thief | tooth | two |
| | towards | type |

## e E

| | |
|---|---|
| ear | exciting |
| earlobe | exclamation |
| early | expensive |
| earth | eye |
| easily | eyebrow |
| east | eyelashes |
| eat | eyes |
| eaten | |
| edge | |
| eleventh | |
| elsewhere | |
| encourage | |
| England | |
| enjoy | |
| enough | |
| evening | |
| ever | |
| every | |
| everybody | |
| everything | |
| example | |
| excitedly | |

## f F

fable
face
faithfully
family
father
fault
favourite
feature
feel
fence
field
fifth
final
finally
fire
fireworks
first
flat
flew
flip
flower
follow

following
foot
football
for
formal
forward
found
four
fourth
friend
friendly
friends
frighteningly
from
front
fruit
further
future

## s S

sadly
safe
said
sandwich
saw
scare
scary
school
Scotland
screamed
second
secondary
section
see
seen
sentence
seven
seventh
shadow
shampoo
sharp
she
shed
ship
shirt
shiver
shocked
shoes
shop
shopkeeper
shopped
shopping
short
should
shoulder

shout
shouted
shouting
show
shower
shriek
silly
sincerely
sir
sister
sixth
skin
skirt
sleep
sleepover
slice
slow
slowly
small
smiled
smooth
snippet
so
some
something
sometimes
somewhere
sound
south
space
sparkling
speak
speaker
speaking
special
speech

spiky
split
spoken
spread
spring
started
starts
stem
still
stop
stopped
stopping
straight
strange
stranger
stuck
study
stupidly
style
subject
such
suddenly
summer
sunny
sure
surprise
surprised
surprising
suspended
swam
swerve
swerving
swimming
swoop